Quarto is the authority on a wide range of topics.

Quarto educates, entertains and enriches the lives of
our readers—enthusiasts and lovers of hands-on living.

www.quartoknows.com

Cover Design: Mandy Norman
Illustrator: David Shephard
Editor: Amanda Askew
Designer: Punch Bowl Design
QED Project Editor: Ruth Symons
Managing Editor: Victoria Garrard
Design Manager: Anna Lubecka

First published in the UK in 2013 by
QED Publishing
Part of The Quarto Group
The Old Brewery, 6 Blundell Street
London, N7 9BH

A catalogue record for this book is
available from the British Library.

ISBN 978 1 78171 702 8
9 8 7 6 5 4 3
HH122019

Printed in China

Picture credits
Shutterstock: Daniiel, 5, 41;
Eliks, 4, 28, 48; Gl0ck, 9;
HAKKI ARSLAN, 19; Javier
Martin, 39; L_amica, 24;
lero, 25; Lukiyanova Natalia
/ frenta, 38; MedusArt, 28;
Merkushev Vasiliy, 18, 43;
Milena_Bo, 12, 28; Mitar
Vidakovic, 20, 21, 44, 45, 46,
47; optimarc, 39; photostOK,
29; Steve Wood, 37; theromb,
41; Valentina Razumova, 31;
Waj, 10; yienkeat, 36

HOW TO BEGIN YOUR ADVENTURE

Are you ready for an amazing adventure – full of mind-bending puzzles, twists and turns – that will test your brainpower to the limit? Then this is the book for you!

Funfair Fright is no ordinary book – you don't read the pages in order, 1, 2, 3... Instead you jump forwards and backwards through the book as the plot unfolds. Sometimes you may lose your way, but the story will soon guide you back to where you need to be.

The story starts on page 4. Straight away, there are puzzles to solve, choices to make and clues to pick up. The choices will look something like this:

IF YOU THINK THE CORRECT ANSWER IS A, GO TO PAGE 10

IF YOU THINK THE CORRECT ANSWER IS B, GO TO PAGE 18

Your task is to solve each problem. So, if you think the correct answer is A, turn to page 10 and look for the same symbol in blue. That's where you will find the next part of the story.

If you make the wrong choice, the text will explain where you went wrong and let you have another go.

The problems in this adventure are about forces, electricity and physics. To solve them you must use your science skills. To help you, there's a glossary of useful words at the back of the book, starting on page 44.

ARE YOU READY?
TURN THE PAGE AND LET YOUR ADVENTURE BEGIN!

FUNFAIR FRIGHT

There's a new funfair in town and you can't wait to check it out. Fellini's Freaky Funfair promises to be the best fairground in the whole world.

FELLINI'S FREAKY FUNFAIR

You're a thrill-seeker and want to go on every ride, no matter how scary. And you're going to take on the funfair's ultimate challenge...

the white-knuckle
DEATH DROP ROLLERCOASTER!

TURN TO PAGE 19
TO START YOUR ADVENTURE...

Waves that move air up and down are called 'transverse waves'. This is true of light, but not of sound.

light waves act like this

sound waves act like this

GO BACK TO
PAGE 20
AND **TRY AGAIN**

No. There's no electricity running through this light bulb.

TURN BACK TO PAGE 27
AND **TRY AGAIN**

No, it doesn't matter that the zombie is lighter. It won't hit the ground first.

It often seems like you have to keep pushing things to keep them moving along, but that's only when other forces act to slow them down.

TURN BACK TO PAGE 36
AND HAVE **ANOTHER GO**

GO BACK TO PAGE 12
AND **TRY AGAIN**

No. When a material such as glass lets light pass through, it is called transparent. You can see clearly through a transparent material.

GO BACK TO PAGE 25
AND **TRY AGAIN**

lets light pass through

Correct! Gravity is the force that makes things fall to the ground and stops you from floating into space.

You'll get to ride the Death Drop Rollercoaster after all!

You jump on a cart and the rollercoaster hauls you to the top of the slope. There's a drooling zombie on the cart in front of you.

Just before you both plunge down the track, you look in the book:

To capture the flesh-eater, you must be heard

While touching its heart, shout out the right word...

Which is the stronger force – magnetism or gravity?

MAGNETISM.
GO TO PAGE 12

GRAVITY.
TURN TO PAGE 17

Correct! Temperature measures how hot or cold something is. It is measured in degrees Celsius or Fahrenheit.

I bought this fair from a strange fellow. I took the machine as part of the deal. No one was ever meant to use it! I will be ruined if you don't catch the monsters. Here are things to help you — The Book and Bottle of Banishment.

You open the book and words form on the first page.

You must answer my questions
and solve the puzzle

To capture the monsters and
end this muddle

The bottle before you will
lock them away

If you say the right words
at the end of the day

It's centuries since the bottle has been opened, and the lid is stuck tight.

How do you loosen it?

HEAT THE LID.
TURN TO PAGE 20

CHILL THE LID.
TURN TO PAGE 43

Plastic is not a magnetic material.

TURN BACK TO PAGE 18 AND **CHANGE YOUR ANSWER**

No. Light normally travels in straight lines. It only bends when it moves from one material to another.

GO BACK TO PAGE 28 AND **TRY AGAIN**

lets light pass through but scatters the light

Yes, that's right. If chameleon monster can make itself translucent, you won't be able to see clearly through its body and the light will be spread out.

You must search for it using a light source.

Which one of these objects would be best to use?

A MATCH.
TURN TO PAGE 23

A TORCH.
GO TO PAGE 29

A FLARE.
HEAD TO PAGE 43

A heavy hand lands on your shoulder, making you jump.

Stop destroying funfair property! I'm taking you to Fellini.

A huge man starts to drag you away. You plant your feet firmly on the ground, so he can only move you inch by inch.

What's making you so hard to drag?

A FORCE CALLED FRICTION
CAUSES YOUR TRAINERS TO GRIP THE GROUND. **GO TO** PAGE 22

THERE'S **A MAGNETIC FORCE PULLING YOU** IN THE OPPOSITE DIRECTION. **TURN TO** PAGE 38

Correct! Smooth and shiny surfaces – such as mirrors – reflect light the best.

Before heading through the door, you check the book to see how you should defeat the chameleon.

To banish the chameleon escapee

Show him his shadow as large as can be

SEEMS EASY ENOUGH. BUT FIRST YOU'LL NEED TO **FIND HIM** ON PAGE 40

Goal! Objects won't move unless they feel
a force, but once an object is moving,
it takes another force to stop it.

1-0

The vampire seems
to have become
taller and her teeth
have grown much
longer and sharper.
Weird...

Question two: If the puck
doesn't need a force to keep it
moving, why does it stop?

THE **FORCE OF FRICTION** WORKS AGAINST
THE OBJECT'S MOTION AND SLOWS IT DOWN.
TURN TO PAGE 16

GRAVITY PULLS ON THE PUCK,
SLOWING IT DOWN.
GO TO PAGE 30

Switches can connect and break a circuit, but the circuit still won't work without power.

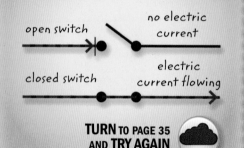

open switch — no electric current

closed switch — electric current flowing

TURN TO PAGE 35 AND TRY AGAIN

Longer wires mean that the battery must push the electrical current through a greater distance of wire, which makes the bulb dimmer.

TURN BACK TO PAGE 39 AND TRY AGAIN

"MAGNETISM!" you shout. But you're not touching the zombie's heart, so it didn't work.

You hold on tight as the rollercoaster races round. Finally, it comes to a standstill and the zombie jumps into your cart. As it leans over you, goo drips from its nose.

You push the zombie overboard and it pulls you with it. You think you must be heavier than the zombie.

Who will hit the ground first?

YOU.
GO TO PAGE 21

THE ZOMBIE.
TURN TO PAGE 5

NEITHER. YOU'LL BOTH LAND AT THE SAME TIME.
FLIP TO PAGE 42

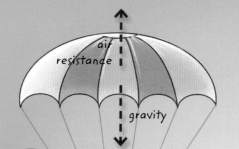

air resistance

gravity

 No, that's not right. When a parachute falls, the upward force of air resistance acts against the downward force of gravity.

TURN BACK TO PAGE 43 AND **TRY AGAIN**

 You feel spinning forces on the chair-o-plane, not gravity.

GO BACK
TO PAGE 41 AND
CHOOSE AGAIN

 Correct! The newton is the unit used to measure forces, and weight is in fact a force!

You pick up the hammer and strike hard. THWACK! But the puck doesn't hit the bell. You start to swing the hammer again, when...

WAIT! You've got to get a second question right for another free go. What unit is used to measure how loud the bell is? Not that you'll ever hit it!

VOLUME.
GO TO PAGE 17

DECIBELS.
TURN TO PAGE 30

Well done! Sound waves *do* bend around corners. That's why you can hear a noise from another room. As you touch the zombie's heart and shout, "*SOUND WAVES!*" the monster transforms into a puddle of liquid. You collect it in the bottle.

All five monsters have been caught, you've ridden the Death Drop Rollercoaster, and you've proved yourself to be the bravest thrill-seeker ever!

You hand the monster-filled bottle and book to Fellini.

This is definitely the best funfair in the world. You should let the monsters free everyday!

MAYHEM MAKER
DO NOT OPEN
DANGER
I don't think so! I'm not a hero like you. As a thank you for saving the fairground, I'd like to give you free entry FOREVER!

No! Turning the nuts clockwise tightens them.

GO BACK TO PAGE 28 AND TRY AGAIN

No! Rubber is an insulator, which means it doesn't conduct electricity. The mummy will be totally unharmed.

GO BACK TO PAGE 37 AND TRY AGAIN

Goal! Even on an air hockey table, friction eventually causes the puck to lose energy.

The vampire smiles, then inches towards you, looking hungrily at your neck.

Beginner's luck. Third — killer — question: If I put one puck on the wooden floor and one on the carpet, which one will need to be pushed harder to get through the doorway?

THE PUCK ON THE **WOODEN FLOOR.**
GO TO PAGE 38

THE PUCK ON THE CARPET.
TURN TO PAGE 18

MOON
GRAVITY SIMULATOR

There's a queue outside the Moon Gravity Simulator. It looks amazing – and it's free! To play, you just have to type in the correct answer on the door panel.

Can sound travel in space?

YES.
TURN TO PAGE 30

NO.
TURN TO PAGE 42

No, volume isn't a unit of measurement. We don't say a sound is '3 volumes' loud — we use another unit instead.

TURN BACK TO PAGE 13 AND **TRY AGAIN**

No, you can lift a paperclip with a weak magnet against the pull of gravity.

THINK AGAIN ABOUT WHICH IS THE STRONGER FORCE ON PAGE 6

That's right! The more you squash a spring, the bigger the push it gives back in the opposite direction.

Gooooood. Question two: Which part of the Mayhem Machine is magnetic?

THE COTTON CLOTHING.
HEAD TO PAGE 33

THE STEEL NAILS.
TURN TO PAGE 28

THE PLASTIC DIAL.
GO TO PAGE 9

 GOAL! The puck needs to be pushed harder to overcome the friction between it and the carpet.

You've beaten the vampire! She screams as she turns into a swirling fog that is sucked into the bottle.

Two down, three to go!

You can hear people shrieking "MUMMY!" from near the bumper cars.

GO TO PAGE 27 TO FIND YOUR **NEXT MONSTER**

That's not right. Think about wood's density – how much mass is squished into a certain volume. Objects with a lower density than water will float.

GO BACK TO PAGE 26 AND **TRY AGAIN**

If the chameleon monster is further from the light source, the shadow will be smaller.

GO BACK TO PAGE 38 AND **HAVE ANOTHER GO**

Time to investigate the funfair. You head towards a test-your-strength machine. You need to hit the striker plate hard enough for the puck to rise and hit the bell.

Test your brain before your brawn with my impossible question. Get it right and you can have a free go.

What is weight measured in?

Thor's
HAMMER STRIKE

GRAMS AND KILOGRAMS.
GO TO PAGE 23

NEWTONS.
TURN TO PAGE 13

No, only a low sound
has a low pitch.

TURN BACK TO PAGE 32
AND **TRY AGAIN**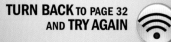

No, a shadow is the dark shape produced
when light is stopped by an object.

GO BACK TO PAGE 40
AND **TRY AGAIN**

Correct! You run the lid under hot water. Heating makes solid
substances expand (get bigger), which makes the lid become loose.

Your heart is beating fast. You turn to the next page of the book.

To find the Spectral
Pirate, you'll have
to find his ship

Find it soon, or he'll
give you the slip

It moves in the same
way as a sound wave

You have to be smart,
and you have to
be brave

**How do sound
waves travel?**

BY MOVING PARTICLES OF AIR
UP AND DOWN.
GO TO PAGE 5

BY MOVING PARTICLES OF AIR
BACK AND FORTH.
TURN TO PAGE 32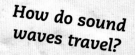

You reconnect the battery and the machine springs to life.

I am the Magnificent Mayhem Maker. You must answer three questions correctly. Make a mistake and I will unleash MAYHEM! Question one: My head is on a spring. If you were to push it down, what would happen?

IT WOULD CREATE A PUSHING FORCE IN THE **OPPOSITE DIRECTION.**
GO TO PAGE 18

IT WOULD CREATE A PUSHING FORCE IN THE **SAME DIRECTION.**
TURN TO PAGE 41

No. The same poles (south and south) repel each other, so the compass needle swings around wildly.

same poles repel each other

opposite poles attract each other

No, it doesn't matter that you're heavier. If you dropped at the same time, you won't fall faster.

both fall at same rate

TURN BACK TO PAGE 31

TURN TO PAGE 12 AND **TRY AGAIN**

Yes, friction is even at work when you walk. It stops you from slipping over.

The man throws you over his shoulder instead and carries you to Fellini. The fairground master is sitting with his head in his hands.

That machine is cursed! You have released five monsters and now you'll have to catch them again. But are you smart enough to complete this quest?

What's the difference between heat and temperature?

HEAT IS THERMAL ENERGY AND **TEMPERATURE** MEASURES HOW HOT SOMETHING IS.
GO TO PAGE 8

TEMPERATURE IS USED TO MEASURE HEAT AND **HEAT** IS SOMETHING HOT.
TURN TO PAGE 36

No, because the surface is dull, it doesn't reflect light as well as a shiny surface.

only some light gets reflected

GO BACK TO PAGE 29 AND TRY AGAIN

No, light travels in straight lines, which is why objects cast shadows and you can't see around corners.

TURN BACK TO PAGE 42 AND TRY AGAIN

No, grams and kilograms are used to measure mass, not weight.

TURN BACK TO PAGE 19 AND TRY AGAIN

Matches don't give off much light and go out quickly.

TURN BACK TO PAGE 9 AND TRY AGAIN

The mummy stands on the steel grate and touches the ceiling. BANG! Metals are great electrical conductors, so the electricity from the ceiling runs through the metal and into the mummy's body. All that is left is a heap of powder, which you collect in the bottle.

Three down, two to go! You look in the book for help...

For the chameleon monster, there's no escape

If you can discover its translucent shape

What does translucent mean?

NO LIGHT PASSES THROUGH.
TURN OVER TO PAGE 37

LIGHT PASSES THROUGH EASILY.
GO TO PAGE 5

SOME LIGHT PASSES THROUGH, BUT IT IS **SCATTERED IN ALL DIRECTIONS.** TURN TO PAGE 9

That's not right. You're in a chamber with less gravity. Think about how astronauts 'bounce' when they walk on the Moon.

GO BACK TO PAGE 42 AND **TRY AGAIN**

Opposite poles (north and south) attract each other, so you can pull the south-pointing needle in any direction you choose using the magnet's north pole.

You tell the pirate about the treasure and show him the compass. You point at the ghost train.

Let's sail for treasure. This wooden beauty will float like a dream. Do ye know why?

FOR THE SAME VOLUME OF WATER, **WOOD HAS LESS MASS.**
GO TO PAGE 39

 WOOD TAKES UP **LESS SURFACE AREA THAN WATER.**
GO TO PAGE 19

The mummy is going crazy on the bumper cars, crashing into the barriers.

This is going to be a tough one! But the book will help.

DODGEMS

To stop the mummy in this park

Strike it with an almighty spark

A spark... that must mean electricity! You have an idea.

MUMMY! I have the power to conduct electricity. Come quietly or you will feel my wrath.

Prove it!

You take a balloon tied up at the pay desk, rub it on your hair and hold it up to a light bulb that's turned off.

What happens?

THE BALLOON POPS
BECAUSE IT GETS ZAPPED
BY THE LIGHT BULB.
GO TO PAGE 5

THE LIGHT BULB LIGHTS UP
BECAUSE ELECTRICITY TRANSFERS
TO THE LIGHT BULB.
TURN TO PAGE 37

Correct! Steel contains iron so it is magnetic (although not all metals are magnetic).

The final question: The nuts of this machine are too tight. Take the spanner on the side. Which way do you turn the nuts to loosen them?

CLOCKWISE.
GO TO PAGE 16

ANTICLOCKWISE.
HEAD TO PAGE 39

Correct! Though you wish he wouldn't sing... The pirate invites you on board.

You sneak a peek at the book first.

To make the pirate
flee with fright

Shine on him the
brightest light

To help you find
. your goal

Add a word to
this hole

When light bounces off a
surface, it has been ....

REFLECTED.
TRY THE GHOST TRAIN ON PAGE 31

ABSORBED.
HEAD TO THE WALTZER ON PAGE 42

BENT.
GO TO THE LOG FLUME ON PAGE 9

You shine the torch around until you spot the blurred shape of a reptile. Chameleon monster realizes that he's been caught. He becomes opaque and dashes into the House of Horrors.

Over the entrance appears a message:
To find the doorway the monster went through, decide which of these is true.

The surface that reflects light the best is…

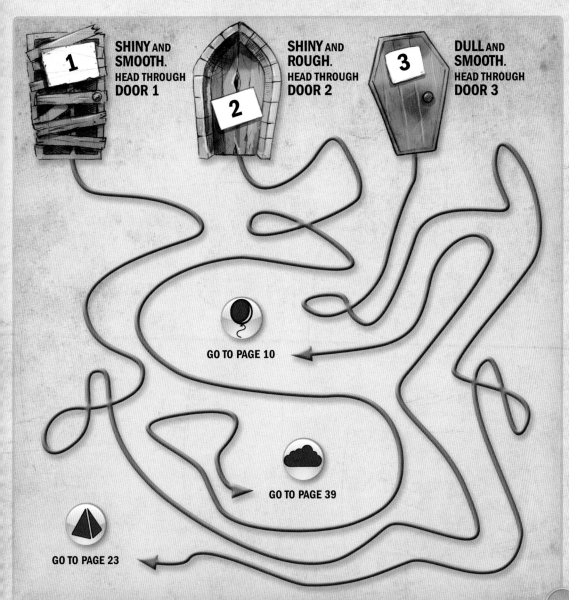

1

SHINY AND **SMOOTH.**
HEAD THROUGH **DOOR 1**

2

SHINY AND **ROUGH.**
HEAD THROUGH **DOOR 2**

3

DULL AND **SMOOTH.**
HEAD THROUGH **DOOR 3**

GO TO PAGE 10

GO TO PAGE 39

GO TO PAGE 23

No, sound travels by passing vibrations from particle to particle, but there are very few particles in space!

GO BACK TO PAGE 17 AND **TRY AGAIN**

No. Gravity is working on all objects, but this isn't what causes the puck to slow down.

GO BACK TO PAGE 11 AND **TRY AGAIN**

Great! When a plane takes off, the roar of its engines measures 140 decibels (dB)!

Grinning, you take a second shot at the striker plate. DING DING DING! You're so excited, you drop the hammer on the attendant's foot.

Thor's HAMMER STRIKE

AHHHHHHH!

"SORRY!" YOU YELL AS YOU **BACK AWAY QUICKLY** TO PAGE 17

Correct! Light reflects, or bounces, off some surfaces. You'll find the brightest light in the funfair on the ghost train.

But how will you get the pirate to the ride? You scan the book for a clue...

But the ghost train is to the north. How will you trick the pirate into thinking it's to the south?

You feel in your pocket and find a magnet and a compass.

To hunt for great treasure, high and low

To the south a pirate will go

Where do you position the magnet to make the compass show due south?

HOLD THE MAGNET'S NORTH POLE TO THE COMPASS'S **SOUTH POLE.**

TURN TO PAGE 26

HOLD THE MAGNET'S SOUTH POLE TO THE COMPASS'S **SOUTH POLE.**

TURN TO PAGE 21

Sound waves are 'longitudinal waves', which vibrate the air back and forth. You must be looking for the swinging pirate ship ride!

Riding in the rigging of the swinging boat is the dreaded pirate.

To join my pirate crew, answer my riddle or I'll cut ye through!

Oh, I sing a sea shanty high, I never go too low. Which way does the pitch of my song go?

A HIGH SOUND HAS A **HIGH PITCH.**
HEAD TO PAGE 28

A HIGH SOUND HAS A **LOW PITCH.**

GO TO PAGE 20

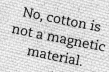

No, cotton is not a magnetic material.

GO TO PAGE 18 **AND TRY AGAIN**

Adding more bulbs shares the battery's electrical energy between more lights, making each bulb dimmer.

TURN BACK TO PAGE 39 AND **CHOOSE AGAIN**

Yes – the mirror is a shiny surface so it reflects light from the chameleon's body to your eyes.

Rubbing your nose, you stand up. There, at the other end of the hall, is chameleon monster again.

This time you know it's a reflection.

But where is chameleon monster standing?

BEHIND THE MIRROR.
GO TO PAGE 36

TO THE LEFT OF THE MIRROR.
TURN TO PAGE 38

Correct!
Your weight depends on the force of gravity. On the Moon, the force pulling you to the surface is weaker, so your weight decreases, making it easy to jump higher!

You feel dizzy when you leave the simulator, so you duck behind a tent where it's quiet.

MAGNIFICENT
MAYHEM MAKER

1893

You notice an old-looking machine, and slide
a coin in the slot. The machine comes to life
for a few seconds before... the lights go out.
You notice some wires sticking out of the side.
The electrical circuit is broken.

Which piece will complete the circuit
and light the bulb again?

BATTERY.

TURN TO PAGE 21

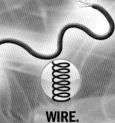

WIRE.

GO TO PAGE 37

SWITCH.

HEAD TO PAGE 12

Think again. Remember, a warm bath can be cooler (at a lower temperature) than a mug of hot coffee, but contains much more thermal energy (heat) because it has more water in it.

TURN BACK
TO PAGE 22 AND
TRY AGAIN

If the chameleon monster were behind the mirror, you wouldn't see a reflection at all.

GO TO
PAGE 33 AND
TRY AGAIN

The pucks on an air hockey table float on a bed of air, so there's no friction or resistance. The next monster must be in the arcade.

The vampire is the scariest monster you've ever seen.

I challenge you to a game of air hockey. The first to three wins. If I win, you go in the bottle. If you win, do your worst!

Easy! To make it more interesting, I'll ask you the three hardest questions I can think of. You get a free shot for each correct answer.

Question one: To keep the puck moving across the table, you must apply a constant force. True or false?

FALSE.
GO TO
PAGE 11

TRUE.
TURN TO
PAGE 5

Correct! When you rubbed the balloon on your hair, you created a static electricity charge. By holding the balloon near the light bulb, the charge jumps from the balloon to the bulb, causing it to light up.

Time to take this bag of bandages down!

Mummy, let's see if you're as powerful as me. This ceiling is electrified to power the bumper cars. I bet you can't touch the ceiling without getting an electric shock. You'll need to stand on something for it to work properly.

I'll beat you easily!

What do you tell the mummy to stand on to be zapped to dust?

STEEL GRATE.
HEAD TO PAGE 24

RUBBER MAT.
TURN TO PAGE 16

Although extra wire will complete the circuit, there still won't be a power source.

TURN BACK TO PAGE 35 AND **TRY AGAIN**

No, when an object stops light from passing through, it is called opaque.

light gets blocked

GO BACK TO PAGE 25 AND **TRY AGAIN**

Your body is not magnetic. This would be impossible unless you were wearing a metal suit and there was a magnet in front of you.

GO BACK TO PAGE 10 AND **TRY AGAIN**

The wooden floor isn't as rough as the carpet. Therefore there is less friction between the puck and the wooden floor – so less force is needed to move the puck.

GO BACK TO PAGE 16 AND **TRY AGAIN**

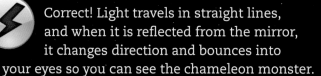

Correct! Light travels in straight lines, and when it is reflected from the mirror, it changes direction and bounces into your eyes so you can see the chameleon monster.

You grab chameleon monster and flick on your torch. Time to shock him with a shadow.

Where should you position the torch to get the strongest shadow?

RIGHT NEXT TO HIM.
GO TO PAGE 41

A FEW PACES AWAY FROM HIM.
TURN TO PAGE 19

No, rough surfaces scatter the light instead of reflecting it back.

GO BACK
TO PAGE 29
AND **TRY AGAIN**

You turn the nuts anticlockwise. As you loosen the last nut, the Mayhem Maker starts to squeal.

The machine glows with a ghoulish blue light. With a whoosh, five monsters fly into the sky.

What have you done?

GO TO PAGE 10 **TO FIND OUT...**

That's right. Wood is less dense than water. The volume of wood in the boat has less mass than an equal volume of water – so it floats.

"But there's no water for it to float on," you shout.

The Spectral Pirate stares at you, dumbstruck. *"To the treasure!"* he screams, as he runs to the ghost train. Now's your chance. You head around the back to find the circuit for the lights.

What changes to this simple circuit will make the bulb brighter?

ANOTHER BULB.
GO TO PAGE 33

AN EXTRA BATTERY.
GO TO PAGE 43

LONGER WIRES.
GO TO PAGE 12

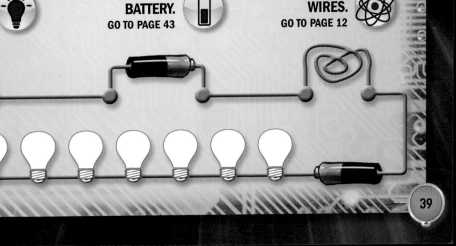

You creep through the maze until you reach the hall of giant mirrors. And sure enough, there's chameleon monster. You dash to catch him, but run, **SMACK**, into a mirror.

If that wasn't the chameleon, what was it?

THE CHAMELEON'S REFLECTION.
GO TO PAGE 33

THE CHAMELEON'S SHADOW.
GO TO PAGE 20

No, when you push down on a spring and let go, it does not stay squashed.

GO BACK TO PAGE 21 AND **TRY AGAIN**

Correct! You plant the torch right in front of chameleon monster and a huge, dark shadow appears on the wall behind it. With a squeal, chameleon monster explodes into a multicoloured cloud, which quickly zooms into the bottle.

Four down, one to go!

You'll find the zombie, easy as can be

On the ride that uses the force of gravity

Which ride will he be on?

THE ROLLERCOASTER.
HEAD TO PAGE 6

THE CHAIR-O-PLANE.
GO TO PAGE 13

No. There's always a little friction slowing you down on the helter-skelter.

TURN BACK TO PAGE 43 AND **TRY AGAIN**

41

Yes! You're in! Space is a vacuum – that means there are not enough particles to carry the vibrations of sound.

When you step inside, a nervous-looking boy asks you a question.

Can we jump higher in here?

YES, OF COURSE.
GO TO PAGE 34

NO, DON'T BE SILLY!
TURN TO PAGE 26

No, 'absorbing' is the opposite to bouncing off a surface.

GO BACK TO PAGE 28

Correct! The acceleration caused by gravity is the same for all objects, so they fall at the same rate.

Luckily, you don't fall far. As soon as you land, you quickly look in the book.

To make the zombie's terror end

Name the type of wave that can bend

LIGHT WAVES.
GO TO PAGE 23

SOUND WAVES.
TURN TO PAGE 14

Flares produce red light, lots of smoke and only work for a limited time.

THERE IS A BETTER CHOICE ON PAGE 9

Chilling makes things contract, or get smaller. This won't loosen the lid.

TURN BACK TO PAGE 8 AND TRY AGAIN

That's right. You add an extra battery to every circuit. The bulbs glow brightly.

You hear the pirate howling in terror. Clutching the bottle, you run to find him. He turns to mist and disappears into the bottle.

One down. Four to go…

You open the book.

To defeat the vampire in an instant

Find where forces act without any resistance

Where on the fairground are resistance forces cancelled out?

THE PARACHUTE DROP.
GO TO PAGE 13

THE AIR HOCKEY TABLE.
TURN TO PAGE 36

THE HELTER-SKELTER.
HEAD TO PAGE 41

GLOSSARY

ACCELERATION
The rate at which the speed of an object increases.

AIR RESISTANCE
Friction between the air and another surface. For example, air resistance slows you down on your bike, making you put in more energy to keep going.

ATTRACTION
When something is pulled towards something else.

CIRCUIT
A complete ring that an electrical current can travel around.

CONDUCTOR
A material that lets heat or electricity pass through it. Metals are good conductors of both heat and electricity.

DECIBEL (DB)
The unit that measures how loud a sound is.

DENSITY
A measurement of how much matter, or 'stuff', is contained in a substance. Density is measured in kilograms (mass) per cubic metre (volume). Dense materials have lots of material packed into a small volume.

ELECTRICITY
A form of energy that can build up in one place as static electricity or flow as an electrical current. Electrical energy can be stored in batteries and it powers electrical devices, such as televisions and computers.

ENERGY
Energy is the drive needed to power things. Moving things have energy, which is why it takes effort to stop them. Energy comes in other forms too, such as light, heat and sound.

EXPAND
To get bigger.

TORCHES, LAMPS AND THE SUN ARE
ALL SOURCES OF LIGHT.

FORCE

An invisible 'push' or 'pull' on an object. Forces cause objects to change speed, change direction or change shape.

FRICTION

A force that stops one surface from sliding easily over another surface. This force slows down moving objects.

GRAVITY

The force of attraction felt between things that have mass. Gravity on Earth makes things fall to the ground. It's what stops us from floating into space.

INSULATOR

A material that does not conduct electricity or heat.

LIGHT

Energy from a source such as the Sun, a flame or a lamp. It allows us to see things.

LONGITUDINAL WAVE

Waves that make particles vibrate back and forth in the same direction as the wave is travelling. Sound waves are longitudinal waves.

MAGNETISM

A force that makes two objects pull towards each other or push each other apart. Metals such as iron and nickel are magnetic materials.

MASS

The amount of matter, or 'stuff', in a substance. Things with more mass are heavier than things with less mass. Because they feel a stronger force of attraction to Earth, they weigh more.

PARTICLE

Everything is made up of particles, far too small for the naked eye to see. For example, air is made of invisible particles of gas.

POLE

One of the two ends of a magnet. A magnet has a north and a south pole. Opposite poles attract each other; like poles repel each other.

REFLECT

To throw back light or sound without absorbing it. For example, a mirror reflects an image back into your eyes, rather than absorbing it.

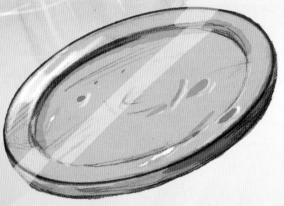

IT'S NEARLY IMPOSSIBLE TO GET RID OF FRICTION – EVEN CONTACT WITH THE AIR WILL EVENTUALLY SLOW DOWN AN AIR HOCKEY PUCK.

REPEL
When a pushing force drives things away from each other.

SHADOW
A dark shape that occurs when something stands between a surface and a light source.

SOUND
Vibrations that travel through the air and can be heard when they reach someone's ear.

STATIC ELECTRICITY
Electrical energy that builds up in one place, but doesn't flow. Static energy sometimes builds up on clothes, giving you a small electric shock when you take them off.

SURFACE AREA
The area covering an object.

TEMPERATURE
The measure of the thermal energy (heat) contained by a substance. Temperature is measured in degrees Celsius and Fahrenheit.

THERMAL ENERGY
The 'internal energy' or heat contained by a substance. Increasing thermal energy increases the temperature of an object.

TRANSVERSE WAVE
Waves that make particles vibrate up and down at right angles to the wave's direction of travel. Light waves are transverse waves.

VACUUM
A volume of space that contains no particles.

VIBRATE
To move back and forth rapidly. Energy travels by making things vibrate. For example, air particles jostle backwards and forwards when they transmit sound.

VOLUME
The amount of space taken up by an object or substance.

WEIGHT
The force of attraction to Earth that an object feels due to its mass.

TAKING IT FURTHER

The Science Quest books are designed to motivate children to develop their Science, Technology, Engineering and Mathematics (STEM) skills. They will learn how to apply scientific know-how to the world through engaging adventure stories. For each story, readers must solve a series of scientific and technical puzzles to progress towards the exciting conclusion.

The books do not follow a page-by-page order. Instead, the reader jumps forwards and backwards through the book according to the answers given to the problems. If their answers are correct, the reader progresses to the next stage of the story; incorrect answers are fully explained before the reader is directed back to attempt the problem once again. Additional support is included in a full glossary of terms at the back of the book.

To support your child's scientific development you can:

- ⚡ Read the book with your child.

- ⚡ Continue reading with your child until he or she has understood how to follow the 'Go to' instructions to the next puzzle or explanation, and is flipping through the book confidently.

- ⚡ Encourage your child to read on alone. Prompt your child to tell you how the story develops and what problems they have solved. Take the time to ask, "What's happening now?"

- ⚡ Discuss how physics works in everyday situations. What types of energy power different machines? What forces act on moving things?

- ⚡ Play STEM-based computer games with your child and choose apps that feature science topics. These hold children's interest with colourful graphics and lively animations as they discover the way the world works.

- ⚡ Most of all, make science fun!